Frankie's Journey
The Silk Road to Napa

*Dear Leslie
+ Alan,
what a Joy to
share my story.
with such special
friends! Enjoy the
Enjoy the journey.
Love
Steph*

Frankie's Journey

The Silk Road to Napa

Stephanie Farrell Grohs and Lauren Coodley

Afterword by Rue Ziegler

The Mousetail Press

©2014 by Stephanie Farrell Grohs and Lauren Coodley

First edition, 2014

The Mousetail Press
Sonoma, California
Themousetailpress.com

Printed in the United States

Publisher's Cataloging-in Publication Data

Grohs, Stephanie Farrell
Frankie's Journey: The Silk Road to Napa, by Stephanie Farrell Grohs and Lauren Coodley, with an Afterword by Rue Ziegler.

ISBN 978-0-9827435-3-9
1. Sericulture - California. 2. Napa Valley (Calif.) - History, local - Rural Conditions. 3. Farm life - California - Napa Valley - History. 4. Silk industry - California. 5. Rural schools - California - Napa County. 6. Petaluma (Calif.) - History. 7. San Francisco Earthquake and Fire, Calif., 1906 - Juvenile fiction.
8. Irish American families - California - San Francisco. 9. Crowley, Denis Oliver, 1852-1928. 10. Hittell, Theodore Henry, 1830-1917. 11. Hittell, Elise C. Wiehe, "Mrs. T. H. Hittell." I. Title. II. Grohs, Stephanie Farrell. III. Coodley, Lauren. IV. Ziegler, Rue.

Dedicated by Stephanie with love and gratitude to my husband Chuck, daughters Katarina and Adaira Grohs; parents Edward Joseph II and Joyce Farrell; and to my brothers Edward Joseph III and Patrick, and my sisters Peggy, Pamela and Ann.

Dedicated by Lauren to the women teachers who gave me courage: Carol Grant and Serena Cochran who *should* have been professors of sociology, and to Nelda Nocita who *was* a professor of economics, and who supported my fight to teach history.

Dear Reader,

Stephanie is a librarian and Lauren a historian. For many years, people have contacted us about letters, diaries, or old buildings that they have uncovered. If someone had discovered this journal in a box, after being in a barn or an attic for close to a hundred years, it would have been grimy, with some pages of the notebook barely readable. There might have been an envelope full of labeled photographs, a blue ribbon, and a piece of what once may have been silk.

But not everyone records their lives in a diary. Everything in our story really happened, but none of the boys who traveled to the St. Joseph's Institute left a record.

In order to tell the story, we invented Frankie and his family. We have accompanied the diary with archival photographs that he might've taken with his pocket Brownie camera. We asked a modern mapmaker, Madeleine Theriault, to create a map of the places in San Francisco that our Frankie lived, while Molly Roy has created a 1908 map of Frankie's journey, so that you, our readers, can see how different travel used to be. Finally, we are delighted that the noted anthropologist Rue Ziegler wrote an Afterword, so that you would know more about the fascinating world that Frankie describes in his wonderful—and imaginary—diary.

Stephanie Farrell Grohs and Lauren Coodley
April 2014

JOURNAL

October 9, 1905

I'm not very sleepy yet. It's hard to write in the dark, but I want to get started. James and the O'Malley twins are snoring, and we have to get up to go to school tomorrow morning—but moonlight is enough for me to see the page.

My name is Francis Patrick O'Connell, but everybody calls me "Frankie". Today was extra special because it was my 10th birthday. I live in a big house for boys called the Youths' Directory on 17th and Howard in San Francisco, right across from Mission Park. It's a four story building run by the Catholic Church, a home for all kinds of kids, not just Irish Catholic boys like us. Each of us boys has a chore. Some help in the kitchen, some do the cleaning, but I work on our newspaper, the *St. Joseph Union*. Father Crowley writes the articles and we have 8,000 subscribers. I fold and stamp the copies.

St. Joseph's Union masthead.

All the boys here have a story. Mine is this: Once my family lived in a house that was "South of the Slot" in San Francisco. The "slot" is what people call the iron crack running the center of Market Street that pulls the street cars. Rich folks live North of the Slot and working folks live South of the Slot. My parents were born in Castlebeara, County Cork, Ireland and sailed to New York in 1880. They traveled by train to San Francisco to be in Father Crowley's parish.

After Da hurt his leg so bad working at the Jackson Brewery, our priest Father Crowley helped us by finding a job for Ma working for the Hittell family. They are rich folks who live near Mission Dolores. Ma cooked and cleaned for them and I mucked the stables. Then Ma died. I miss her every day. Two years ago Father Crowley brought James and me to live in the Youths' Directory.

For my birthday, Father Crowley arranged for my whole family to be together at the Hittell's grand home. The large round table in the dining room was set with china and crystal. Between my younger brother James and my older sister Fiona was my Da. He was sitting straight with his broad shoulders back and large tough hands folded. I looked across the table and he winked at me. We both smiled.

My sister Fiona looks young for being 13 years old. She has my Ma's black wavy hair, fair skin and blue eyes. Folks call that Black Irish. James is a year

Frankie's World

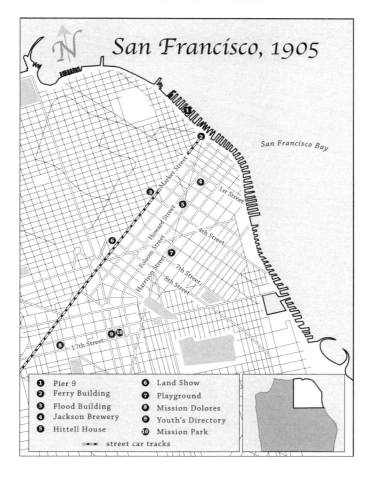

San Francisco, 1905

San Francisco Bay

Market Street
1st Street
Howard Street
4th Street
Folsom Street
Harrison Street
7th Street
8th Street
17th Street

❶ Pier 9
❷ Ferry Building
❸ Flood Building
❹ Jackson Brewery
❺ Hittell House
❻ Land Show
❼ Playground
❽ Mission Dolores
❾ Youth's Directory
❿ Mission Park

street car tracks

younger than me. Just like Da, he has copper color hair and green eyes and you can tell that he's going to be tall. That leaves me somewhere in the middle with thick brown hair and blue eyes. The only thing I have in common with the two redheads in my family are the freckles.

Mr. Hittell, his grown-up daughter Catherine, and Father Crowley complete the circle. Catherine baked my favorite cake, apple spice with raisins and buttercream frosting. Da can whistle any tune and everyone joined into a chorus of "Happy Birthday". The ten candles were burning and wax was starting to drip when I closed my eyes, made a wish, and blew them out all at once.

Presents were next. Da gave me a pocketknife with a whale bone handle, Mr. Hittell and Catherine gave me a new pair of knickers, jacket and cap since I had shot up 3 inches this year. Fiona gave me a pair of mittens she had knitted and James gave me a box of my favorite Cracker Jacks. When I opened the package that Father Crowley had carefully wrapped in brown paper and string, I found this book bound in leather. He called it a journal. He said that in this new century, boys would need to be able to read and write well to make a living and that a smart lad like me should practice and describe my adventures. I don't have to write everyday but I want to give it a try before I go to sleep.

January 15, 1906

It's not so easy keeping a journal. I had to ask Father Crowley what to write about, and he suggested that I just describe one day in my life. He handed me a surprise—a Brownie camera so I could take pictures and remember everything, just like a reporter! So I'll give it a try...

My first thought in the morning is baseball. The boys made me the captain of the team even though I am not the best player. That really riles James. My second thought is getting my oatmeal while it is still hot.

I get up every morning and dress. We don't have to wear uniforms, but most of the clothes are real nice hand me downs, clean and neat. The little ones are always losing their caps and tripping over their shoe laces, so we help them. We have to get ready to go to school at eight, and do all of our chores before that. We walk four blocks to Mission Primary School. Boys from the Youths' Directory have to get good grades and behave ourselves.

We pass my favorite bakery, Zeller's, right before we get to school. And sometimes, I stop and get a bag of doughnut holes for a treat. Reading and writing come easy but arithmetic isn't my favorite.

James doesn't even have to use a pencil and paper, it just happens in his head like magic. Father Crowley says we are all blessed with a gift, and like my Da, my gift is being with horses.

After school, we walk home quickly to do afternoon chores, and rush to the lot to play ball—I wish there were grass. When we slip and fall trying to catch the ball, it hurts on the concrete! There are lots of tall buildings in our neighborhood, and we worry about breaking windows with the baseballs.

My baseball team.

At 5 o'clock the mission bells ring, letting us know that it is time to come home for supper. Some of the boys have to help carry out the heavy and hot dishes from the kitchen. I am glad to get my newspaper stamping chore done earlier so I can eat

first. After the dishes are washed and put away, we
gather in the parlor where there is a crackling fire.
We sit in a circle on the carpet while Father Crowley
settles in his rocker, lights his pipe and begins story
telling. Father Crowley is always dressed in a black
suit, hat, black shoes, and a white Roman collar. He is
a big man, tall and broad. He has wavy gray hair, and
is clean shaven. He is the kind of man that all people
want to talk to because of his kind smile and
twinkling eyes.

Tonight, he told us our favorite story, the one
we never get tired of, about his life before he was a
priest. When he was 18, he sailed from Castelbeara,
Ireland to Boston with his mates to find his fortune.
In Boston, he found a job at a printing house. Then,
at the age of 23, they sailed again by way of Panama,
hiking though the jungles, to the gold and silver
mines on the West Coast of America. His dream was
to become a priest and it came true when he hit pay
dirt. If it wasn't for that mine in Nevada, none of us
would be here.

April 6, 1906

I opened up my leather bag and just found this journal. I wasn't sure if it survived the earthquake… and everything is packed so tightly in this tent.

Here's what I remember of that morning when everything changed. I woke up from my deep sleep with a start when I heard horses whinnying and shifting outside as if they were in pain. There was a deep rumbling in the distance, like rolling thunder. The room started shaking; our bed was sliding, tossing books, basin, and crucifix to the floor. In the first few moments, I thought I was in a shipwreck. The rolling of the floor continued for what seemed like an eternity and James clung to me stiff with fright. Next came a pounding on the door, and the loud, clear voice of Father Crowley calling, "Boys—it's an earthquake, get dressed, tie your shoes, gather your gear, and come downstairs immediately!"

We didn't say a word as we jumped up, dressed quicker than we ever had. I grabbed my hat and a coat, picture of my Ma, my journal, and flew down the stairs. All of us boys were gathered in the front hall and Housekeeper Mary called out our names to make sure no one got left behind. Father Crowley opened the front door and led us out to the sidewalk. What we saw outside was a large crack running down the street—one side had shifted forward and the other side had sunk. No horse could travel down that street since the trolley tracks had bent and broke. All our neighbors were piling out of their buildings. Some of them must have been awful scared to run out in their night clothes. Not everyone had the chance to grab their belongings. The littlest boys started to cry as the buildings around us crumbled, with chimney bricks falling down wherever we looked. The church bells were still ringing wildly as Father Crowley scooped up the smallest boy, baby Samuel, in his arms. He led us all to Mission Park so we could be out of danger.

How wrong I was. Even worse than the shaking ground was the sight of flames and smoke filling the sky. We huddled together trying to keep from choking. The smoke and soot burned our eyes and filled our lungs. We covered the kids' faces with our handkerchiefs, and that helped a little. We could hear sirens and knew that our city was burning. That morning, the sunshine was dimmed by the dark smoke. I never saw so many grown people, even men and boys, cry.

Our house and torn-up street the morning of the earthquake.

April 20, 1906

Here at Mission Park, all the families live outside in tents. With our city being flattened by the fire, there isn't any place to go. The day of the earthquake, Father Crowley and Mr. Rolfe told the soldiers to let us pitch tents and start a food kitchen. Every available hand along with us boys set up the soup kitchen in Rolfes barn. It seems like we are going to be eating all our meals outside for a long time. In the camp, we have to get up before it's light. We have morning prayer, then begin to haul water, gather firewood, and go up to the kitchen to help fix breakfast. We don't have any time to do lessons anymore; it seems one meal ends and another one starts. For breakfast, we serve mush and milk with hot biscuits. For dinner at noon, hash, vegetables, and bread. For supper, plates are filled with Irish stew with more biscuits.

I waited the longest time just to hear news of my Da and Fiona. My sister was safe with the Hittells and I learned that their house had very little damages, and the horses were just fine. I was scared about Da, he had disappeared. He wasn't in his rooming house. Later, we got word that he was trapped at the old Union racetrack. You see, he went there early to try to make a little money cleaning stables. It's a good thing he was trapped, because dozens of fires were burning South of the Slot. Blocks and blocks of wooden houses were set ablaze, including the one he lived in. My Da lost his house!

The family in the next tent at Mission Park.

October 12, 1906

After the Great Fire was put out, Da was able to come here and live near James and me in a tent, with other men who had lost everything. Da is going to be moved into one of the new boarding houses that are being built, while we are going to move back into the repaired Youths' Directory. I am surprised to say this, but I really do miss school. I mostly miss baseball and going to the Hittell house to groom the horses. Lots of the boys from the Directory have made new friends but it's just not like the old days. I can't wait to move back into my old room.

Mission Park now looks like a small city. Some folks have sewing machines in front of their tents, others have baby carriages. Everyone has some place to hang their laundry to wash and dry. Father Crowley is very busy working with the Mayor trying to get the city back on its feet. He tells us that we are a part of rebuilding the dream: San Francisco will be more beautiful than ever.

Today I got a letter from my big sister Fiona. I knew it was from her right away from the curlicues all over my name. Da and James were there peeking over my shoulders as I opened the letter. She wrote "Catherine and me are up to our elbows in flour and yeast working in the kitchen with the two ovens, baking bread for the soup kitchen. I hope that you are getting fresh food and clean water. I miss you, James, and Da. I will send money for you as soon as I can. Knickers is still looking for me every morning for a carrot." They say the Post Office never lost a letter during the earthquake, and now I know it's true.

James caught trouble today. I went into our tent to find my whalebone jackknife so I could cut some string for tying up the flour sacks. As usual, my side of the tent was neat but the box I keep near my bedroll was open and my knife was gone. I was mad as the blazes and ran out to find James in the sandlot near the street. I just knew he would be with the gang and I wouldn't be surprised if he was playing stick knife. I found the boys standing in a circle with James in the middle. He had his cap pushed back on his head and I saw the sun glinting on the knife blade as he laughed and tossed it up high in the air. He didn't move a muscle as it landed between his feet.

He whistled *Yankee Doodle* just like Da as he passed his cap around to collect his winnings. The blade landed just 1 inch away from his right boot. I broke through the circle, grabbed his ear, and dragged him to where Da was working. I sure hope Da gives him the whipping he deserves.

April 29, 1907

What a night! I didn't expect to see hundreds of people come to the big surprise welcome we had for Father Crowley. The new playground was lit up while two hundred of us sang:

"Home again home again from a foreign shore;
O it fills my heart with joy to meet my friends once more..."

Home Again is one of Father Crowley's favorite songs. The Mayor, the Hittells, and the newspaper people all circled around with us. It made the headlines that Father Crowley returned from Rome, where he actually met the Pope.

Clipping of Father Crowley
returning from Rome.

Last year, Father Crowley had a bully idea to build something he called a "playground" in our neighborhood. It is the first one in San Francisco. Mrs. Hayward, who helps out with the paper, always complained that us kids teased the stray dogs and cats in our neighborhood because we had nowhere to play. I remember how we all sat around the kitchen table eating our apple pie as Father Crowley started to sketch the playground. We really needed better fields if we were going to beat the Italian kids from St. Vincent's! My fielding and hitting have improved so much since I was able to practice at Mission Park before we moved back here to the Youths' Directory.

Now that it's done, my favorite part is the three baseball diamonds with steel backdrops. James and some of the younger boys are keen on the basketball courts. We even have a club room with an open fireplace, kitchen, and a shower. I am so excited that me and the other boys have a sports field where we won't catch heck for breaking windows. The playground is on six acres between Sixth and Harrison Streets. I can see it from my bedroom window.

I am twelve now and I have another job working the stables at the Hittell home after school. I'm in charge of mucking the stalls and providing oats and hay and water for the evening feed. Besides, I get to see Fiona and Miss Catherine after work and send money home to Da, like Fiona does.

May 9, 1908

Today, after I finished the job at the stables, gave Knickers his lump of sugar, and walked home, Tommy O'Leary bolted in and told me to go straight to Father's study. Had I done something wrong? My heart was pounding. When I saw my Da with Mr. Hittell and Father Crowley, I knew something had happened. James was standing next to Da looking down at his shoes. What had he done? When I looked up, everyone was smiling so it couldn't be bad news.

Father Crowley told James and me that we had been chosen to be part of the journey to the ranch in Rutherford! You see, he wanted us boys to have a way to earn a living as we grow up, so he had an idea to start a farm school for us. The school is named after St. Joseph. Father Crowley's idea is for us to learn how we can become successful farmers. A farmer needs to know how to plant crops, raise pigs, cattle, and chickens, and to manage accounts. These are things that you just can't learn out of books. At the ranch, we will take classes every morning and do chores in the afternoon. Already at the school, there's a big house for us to live in with the boys who went up earlier, a barn for the animals, and a chapel.

Thirty of us boys will leave early tomorrow morning to join the school. Father Crowley says that we will love being on the land. I don't know about that. I have never been out of San Francisco, not even to Oakland. I heard the older boys from the ranch talking about how dark it is at night and how you hear screaming when a mountain lion catches a rabbit. What if that mountain lion caught me? I don't think my jack knife is going to stop it. What if something happens to James?

What does my Da think about all this? I looked at his face and I couldn't tell if he was really happy or hiding his sadness. One side of his mouth was turned up and the other side down. He walked over to James and me, wrapped his arms around us, and told us that we will all be fine. "Mr. Hittell's brother John owns another ranch nearby in Napa. I know that he will be be looking out for Father Crowley and you."

May 10, 1908

I feel the waves rocking the boat up here on the hurricane deck. I'm sitting close to the big smokestack and James is standing closer to the edge looking back at San Francisco. My stomach is going up and down and it doesn't help to look at the horizon like the sailors said. James and I climbed up to the top deck so we could see better and I could have some quiet to write. When we boarded the ferry this morning with the other boys, Father Crowley said we could explore but we had to stay on the main deck. But it was very crowded and the salt air smelled so fresh I couldn't help climbing the steps. Besides, in my favorite book, *Kidnapped,* the hero would be on the top deck.

Last night, I was so excited I couldn't sleep. My kit was packed next to my cot. This would be my first time boarding a boat. I fell asleep only to have James shake me awake. We said our goodbyes and left to walk down Market Street. We had to share the street with horse-pulled streetcars, carriages, and noisy automobiles. Usually, the only time I walk on Market Street is on St. Patrick's Day when we march in the parade. This morning it was barely light and the city was already smelling of coffee and fresh bread.

We gathered under the clock of the Ferry
Building, picked up our tickets, and climbed aboard
the *General Frisbee*. Father Crowley carried a saddle
and bridle that his friend Mrs. Hittell gave him years
ago. I was the last in line and I wasn't sure that I
would make it on deck before the ferry pulled away.

Last view of San Francisco before we leave!

Here on the boat, I can hear the sea gulls cry
and the foghorns blow off Alcatraz Island way out in
the Bay. The fog isn't as thick as it is in summer so I
can still see the lights on Fisherman's Wharf as
boats and fishermen start their day. I am trying not
to feel homesick as the city starts to disappear from

view. I will be away from land for two hours and I can't wait to get off this rolling boat. I'm not meant to be a pirate!

When the boat finally docks, it will be late morning in a place called Vallejo. I sure wish that there were money enough to take the train to Rutherford where the train station is only a half a mile from the farm. But, when I asked Father about it, he explained that our tickets cost 75 cents for each person which was all the money the Youths' Directory had to spend on this adventure. Besides we are picking up some farm animals in Vallejo to take with us. I sure hope that I can tramp miles and miles into the wilderness.

I never thought I'd be sorry to see the back of a boat!

May 11, 1908

My legs are dangling out of the hayloft of the Spreckels' Stock Farm barn. I'm balancing my journal on my knees. We've made it as far as Napa. When the ferry tied up, we stepped onto a long pier, surrounded by marshy pools full of croaking frogs. All thirty of us walked off the ferry in single file. Were we glad there was a group of lads who knew Father Crowley to meet us from St Vincent Ferrars' Parish in Vallejo! It almost looked like a parade. At the head were two men on horseback prodding seven enormous cows towards us. At the end there was a horse, but a very different kind than the ones who pulled the Hittell carriage. They called her a Palomino. I knew how to help Father tack her, but she buckarooed when he climbed on. The rest of us, kids and cows, had to walk.

We started walking as the sun rose over the marshes. We stopped to cross the river at Suscol, where we found a wharf and a hotel. Crossing the Napa River on a raft took several trips for the animals, boys, and Father Crowley. Finally, we hiked on a track toward the sun, past fields with a strange new smell. "This is what alfalfa, oat hay, and sweet corn smell like," said Father Crowley. We tramped eleven miles; the longest walk of my life.

Mr. Spreckels is an old friend of Father Crowley: they both helped build parks in San Francisco. His mansion is on a small hill overlooking the valley with a verandah wrapped around. I can see the paddocks where the horses graze and beyond, the river. I can almost see the San Francisco Bay.

Mr. Spreckels gave me this postcard of his farm where we spent our first night. Dr. Leggo and Sevens live in this barn.

I can hardly believe that I was allowed to groom and feed some of the most famous horses in the world: Solitaire and his son Voorhees, Dr. Leggo, and Sevens, named for Mr. Spreckels' winning hand in a game of cards!

After I finished grooming the horses, I walked over to thank Mr. Spreckels. Standing next to him was a man he introduced as Mr. Henry Wheatley.

Father Crowley gave a low whistle when Mr. Spreckels told us that Wheatley's Shires up near Yountville had swept the gold medals at the State Fair last year. "He'll make more money breeding horses than he will with lawyering" he joked. Mr. Wheatley shook my hand and invited us boys to his ranch after we settle. He said I had a fine touch with the horses. Da would be so proud of me! Our bedrolls are in the hay and I'm ready for sleep.

May 12, 1908

This morning we left the horse farm and started our journey into the town of Napa for supplies. We stopped at Herman Schwartz' store, and saw 150 different kinds of pocket knives. Mr. Schwartz sells stoves, glass, and fruit cans at what he calls "San Francisco prices." At his store, we met other farmers and fishermen.

Just like in San Francisco, we saw many Chinese people. We bought some penny candy at Lai Hing Co. Store by the river. Seven wharves stood along the waterfront, along with lumber yards, tanneries and warehouses. We saw a steamer carrying an entire flock of sheep. We attended Mass at St John the Baptist Church on Main Street, where Father Slattery blessed our journey. Father Crowley knows everybody! North of the church, we piled our belongings on a wooden raft and all jumped into the Napa River. We had to push the cows into swimming—they were that scared!!

On the other side of the river, Italian families were selling vegetables like those we hope to grow ourselves. We bought some cucumbers and tomatoes for the journey. When we had only walked for a mile or so, what did we see but a new bridge being built! It was over the river at Monticello Creek.

Here's what the Napa River Wharf looked like.

We kept going another three miles up to this cave, right where the mountains begin. Father Crowley says this road, Silverado Trail, was once used by real Indians walking up the valley to get obsidian for their arrows.

As we rolled out our bedrolls an hour ago, James thought he heard a bear behind our cave near the oak trees. He was sure it was a grizzly! So, I hushed my voice and began the story of Samson, Lady Washington, and Ben Franklin, the bears Mr. Hittell knew in San Francisco. The boys' eyes opened very wide when I told how these wild bears lived not far from us. Samson was enormous and weighed 1500 pounds! He was captured when he was grown and held in a cage. The other two grizzlies were taken when cubs and then tamed by the owner. Mr. Hittell noticed that the fur was worn off the backs of the tame bears and was amazed to learn they had been used as pack animals. The owner even rode them. I mysteriously ended my story: "Of course, you know they escaped…" Tommy said he didn't believe me and the boys bravely went to sleep. Me and Father are the last two awake by the campfire.

Frankie's Journey

0   5   10 mi
0   5   10 km

Rutherford ❽
St. Joseph's School

NAPA RIVER

❼ Caves

❻ St. John's Church
❺ Lai Hing Co. Napa
❹ Spreckels' Farm
❸ River crossing Suscol

PETALUMA RIVER

SAN PABLO BAY

❷ Vallejo

PACIFIC OCEAN

SAN FRANCISCO

SAN FRANCISCO BAY

❶ Ferry Building

❶ Ferry Building
❷ Vallejo Wharf
❸ River crossing
❹ Spreckels' Farm
❺ Lai Hing Co.
❻ St. John's Church
❼ Caves
❽ St. Joseph's School

May 15, 1908

I keep my journal in the drawer of my swell new desk. I've been at the farm for a few days so I thought it was time to write. There's plenty of sunlight that comes in my dormitory room. I only have to share a room with one other boy: naturally, they put me with James. It's been strange getting used to this new place. I think I miss being in the city more than I expected. It seems so quiet here. There are no little boys running around tripping over their shoelaces. I can't go to a bakery like I used to, or hear the streetcar clanking up the street. Crickets sound as loud as the trolley cars. I haven't seen a newspaper since I left San Francisco.

The day after we left the cave, we finished the walk up to Rutherford. Just after sunset, we found the long driveway. Father Crowley happily slid off his saddle and announced to the parade of cows and boys behind him that we were home. In front of us stood a tall house. Brother Paul came out the front door carrying a lantern. Boys tumbled down the stairs shouting hello and asking our names. We trooped into the kitchen where the long tables were set up with the grandest meal ever.

I took this picture when we got to our school
in Rutherford at last!

Here's what a day at the farm is like: Father
Crowley thinks growing boys need our rest, so we
sleep past the roosters till 6:30 in the morning. That
is, except for the dairy boys, who milk the cows in the
creamery at 5:00. The birds are out and singing, and
even the bees are humming on the locust blossom,
getting ready to settle down to their work of
gathering honey. We do chores until our breakfast at
8 o'clock. We go to school all morning. Afternoons,
we work in the gardens, hoeing the weeds and
spreading manure; we help build gravel walks and
fences and feed the chickens. We are painting the
barns yellow and red. The tower clocks will be
placed on the cupola of the granary. Their bells will
be heard all the way into Rutherford. No excuse
then for being late!

At this new school, the Brothers are very strict. We don't have a lot of free time. The best part about being here is that I am learning to do so many things with my hands. Here in Rutherford, I go to bed every night plum tired. My eyes close the minute the birds Father Crowley says are white crown sparrows and lute scented warblers settle into the great oaks outside my window.

SUNSET MAGAZINE

Work calls them again from four to six

At the Rutherford farm, at present, the boys assist practical farm hands. They are up at five. After breakfast dairy work, viticulture or horticulture awaits them. At noon they rest for two hours; to the swimming pond they go at three. Work calls them again from four to six; after supper they play baseball, read or lounge, and at half-past eight, they are expected to be in bed. The boys seem perfectly happy with their country life. It lacks all the unpleasant side of child life in an institution.

CARRYING MILK TO THE CREAMERY

Clipping of St. Joseph's School from Sunset Magazine

February 14, 1909

Miss Catherine arrived today in the Hittell's grand carriage to visit us. I was so excited to see her! She traveled with the President of the Ladies Silk Society, Mrs. Murphy. Miss Catherine brought James and me our favorite root beer soda and Ghirardelli chocolate from Fiona. Along with the treats, she brought mulberry cuttings for the school to plant.

Many people throughout the Napa Valley and California are planting mulberry trees to earn money. The Ladies Silk Society is paying folks to grow these trees. A teacher will arrive here from Switzerland in June to teach us boys how to raise worms. Then we can sell the silk from the cocoons to the factory in Petaluma. The breeding of the worms can only be done in spring and summer so he better get here soon. Already our new hatchery is almost built and is just waiting for red and yellow paint. Miss Catherine and Mrs. Murphy pulled out their camera and took a lot of photographs of what we had done. Tomorrow, we will plant the trees and put up shakes to protect the tender bark.

At dinner with us boys, Miss Catherine laughed as she told us about a family that lived in Browns' Valley near Napa who ordered 50 cuttings to plant. When they arrived, there wasn't room for more than

5 plants. The farmer complained that they'd never be able to make a living harvesting so few trees. She didn't want to disappoint him further by explaining it takes four years for the trees to produce enough leaves to sell. He sent her packing with the extra cuttings that she left along her route in St. Helena.

I'm in bed now with just enough light to write in my journal. Miss Catherine left me with her mother's book, *California's Silk Grower's Instructor*. I remember how she and her friends used to meet every week to talk about how silk production could change California. Mrs. Hittell even knew how to doctor a worm! I wonder how you do that?

May 20, 1909

Stanley has a mouth as big as a carp. Ever since his family sent him, a rich kid from Palo Alto, here, he has been poking fun at us. The latest trouble started yesterday when our neighbor Mrs. de Latour from the ranch next door, brought the newspaper for Father Crowley to see. I've seen her at Mass on Sunday at Holy Family Church. Funny, I think I remember her from Mrs. Hittell's parlor when my Ma served the tea and cakes to the Ladies Silk Culture Society. I remember peeking past the kitchen door to see what cakes were left. That was a long time ago.

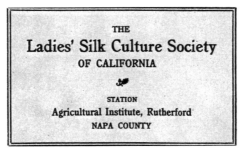

The Ladies Silk Culture Society ran another school where girls raise cocoons in Piedmont. After class this morning, Stanley told us that silk is girls work. Truthfully, I figured I just better punch him before James did. It felt swell. My best mate Robby pounded me on the back.

Brother Richard read the article from the *Pacific Rural Press* to us in Agronomy class. The reporter liked our chances of us being able to make silk:

> Crowley has a lot of wide-awake boys in his charge, and they are to be kept busy with the worm feeding and spinning and can demonstrate what can be made out of it. . . If Father Crowley cannot make it work with his boys, the Silk Culture Society had better go to sleep again for a generation or until we have people who cannot make easy money in ways they like better than caterpillars.

My Da didn't know about easy money. Before he married my Ma, he worked as a bareknuckle boxer. Many bedtimes, he told us of his boxing adventures. He was at the Sharkey-Fitzsimmons match in the mechanics pavilion in 1897 where the referee was the famous gunslinger Wyatt Earp. Police had to remove a gun from Mr. Earp's jacket before the match. It was rumored that Earp threw the match for the Irishman Sharkey by ruling that Fitzsimmons threw a foul blow. Da always laughs that neither of the boxers got the prize money because bareknuckle boxing was still illegal in California.

Miss Catherine left this picture of the Piedmont School
with me.

August 10, 1910

I can't sleep. I'm feeling guilty. I purposely destroyed the United States Mail. Here's how it happened: This morning Robby was sitting across the table from me. I thought something was wrong with him because he kept tapping his nose and crossing his eyes when I looked up from my stack of flapjacks. Then I got it, he was giving me the secret signal. That meant that we meet behind the Chapel. He held up two fingers to signal that the meeting time was 2 o'clock. I never knew with Robby what he had up his sleeve. On the way out the door he told me to grab my fishing pole and some bait so it would seem normal for us to be at the river. He had something to show me.

After finishing my Saturday chores and digging near the chicken coop for some worms, I headed out for the river. Robby was waiting for me at our best fishing spot near some willow trees that make it shady. All he said while I baited my hook was "Did anyone follow you?" I told him no. He reached into his pants pocket and pulled out a wrinkled envelope.

"I think it's a map or a list of spies," he whispered. "Brother Patrick gave me a dozen eggs to deliver yesterday and a book for Mrs. Tuttle. I had just crossed the road and was lifting the latch on their door when I dropped the book. This envelope fell out. In the return address corner there were the initials GL. I think it's written in code."

It was true that Brother Patrick isn't usually in charge of the egg delivery so something did seem suspicious. "I think it's our duty to open the letter," Robby said. He sliced it open with his pocket knife and started reading.

Dear City Chaps,

We work in the vegetable garden down near the old bridge on the banks of the Napa. Stanley and myself have charge of watering. That's what irrigation means. We raise an acre of cabbages, half that area of peas; lettuce in plenty; onions enough to gladden the heart of a garlic-eating nation, radish without stint, Hubbard squash, tomatoes of the Livingstone Beauty persuasion, and about three acres of Irish potato.

I was listening so closely that I didn't notice the line on my pole jerking up and down.

We burst out laughing, put the rest of the pages back in the envelope, and sent it floating down the river. We told ourselves that it's just a slower way to deliver a letter. Now here I am and I'm tossing and turning. GL stands for Gabriel Lloyd, the only boy here with those initials. I'm hoping we can make it right. First thing in the morning, I've got to find him. I better go to Confession.

June 4, 1911

I was in the newspaper! I might even be famous! I'm lying here in my bed with James asleep, but I keep going over in my mind the part of the newspaper article that was about me.

You see, Helen Dare, the famous lady reporter from *The San Francisco Call*, came to visit us last week. Miss Dare once catapulted down a lumber flume tied to a log. She rode posse in pursuit of a stage-robbing bandit, and she even sat up all night in a haunted house! She was also the first lady to cover the horse races. That is how she met Mr. Hittell and Mr. Spreckels.

Today, the newspaper she wrote for, *The San Francisco Call*, came in the mail. We sat at supper around the campfire, reading the funny parts and laughing. Teddy raised his voice up like Miss Dare's and recited:

A lean weedy boy of grave demeanor—the steady eyed sort of boy you can trust with anything—came out of the little stone building that holds the incubators, carefully closing the door behind him and carrying in his hands a pan full of chicken feed. He was on his way to a chicken run, but he stopped to pick up a young pigeon and coddle it in the hollow of his arm, and again, to put his long arm through a gateway around the neck of a lame fawn and press its lovely head against his faded blue shirtfront.

Boy did I squirm and the little ones giggled when Teddy asked us "Ain't that sweet?

One thing Miss Dare got right was how we say "our" about everything here—from the butter to the pigs. She wrote, "If you get away with the wrapper stamped *Rutherford Creamery* and bearing the picture of a stone doorway with a cow on one side and a boy on the other, you may be sure that it is college [our] butter and nothing else." When she was here, we had just gotten real money for our farm butter. We started with those 7 cows and now we have 250! We have gone from 2 pigs to more than 100 who dash out from unexpected hiding places and trip visitors. We were that embarrassed when Miss Dare stumbled on one of them. There are 600 chickens now, instead of the 6 or 7 that we bought in a crate.

We get paid for cutting the leaves from the mulberry trees and feeding the silkworms in our hatchery every morning. With the sun pouring in through the big windows, and the furnace, keeping it warm for the worms to live, we like going inside because it's always cozy!

Father Crowley tells us that if we work hard, we'll be able to support ourselves and bring more boys. Butter, poultry, beef, hay and grain are what will do it. We make 1000 pounds of butter to sell to market. We pack it in brown paper and stamp the packages before we cart them from the creamery to the wagon where they will go to the train station in Rutherford. When we hear the whistle, we know that our precious cargo is on its way to San Francisco. A couple of the older boys get to travel with Brother Paul to the wharf in Napa City to see our butter on its way. I can't wait for my turn.

Clipping of Helen Dare in the Yukon from
San Francisco Examiner

October 21, 1912

I was finally chosen to take the train—just this once!—with boxes of silk threads. From Rutherford Station, Brother Paul and I stopped in Schellville and changed trains.

I almost missed the train taking this picture!

In Petaluma, we stepped off the coach for good and walked the half mile to the Carlson Currier Silk Mill, a three story red brick building on the river. Petaluma, like Napa, has a river that flows through the town and empties into the San Francisco Bay. It is very shallow and windy but it is the third busiest river in California. Folks are shipping fruit, wheat, eggs, and now silk from the brick mill on Lakeville Highway and Jefferson Street.

When we opened the heavy doors to the factory, we saw rows of girls seated at their benches working at the spinning. My ears were ringing. The noise was deafening, it was hard to think with the whirring and the clanking of these giant pieces of metal. But then, a girl with big dark eyes looked up and smiled. I looked around but I was the only one standing. I quickly put my boxes down as she came over and said "Thank you for the delivery. We sure appreciate the fine silk you grow at your farm. I am Stella. Mrs. Murphy tells me you are one of Father Crowley's boys."

Here are the Petaluma girls at their machines.

I looked at her blankly and asked, "How do you know Mrs. Murphy?" She laughed and said her family came from Italy and still lived South of the Slot. Her Ma had got a job working for Mrs. Murphy's Silk School on Market Street. I told her my family lost our house in the earthquake and now they live in the Mission. We got talking about what we remembered of the quake, and suddenly I had to run all six blocks to meet Brother Paul and catch the train.

I'm sitting here writing as the miles go by, returning from Petaluma to Rutherford. There are marshes all around that remind me of what it looked like when we first arrived in Vallejo so many years ago. It's funny how the Petaluma River goes all the way to the San Francisco Bay and Stella and I both came from San Francisco. She sure has beautiful, dark eyes.

Here's where we bring the raw silk.

October 5, 1913

I will be 18 this year. I am able to travel in just a few days with Stella to bring our silk to the San Francisco Land Show. Stella and I have been writing letters since we first met. Her parents came from Italy to San Francisco, settling in my old neighborhood. They dreamed of opening a restaurant and struggled to keep their family of eight together. With the help of the Boys and Girls Aid Society, she and her mother enrolled for training to work with silk. Mrs. Rienzi, the manager of the school at the Flood Building, works for the Ladies Silk Society. Stella learned to care for the silkworms and wash the silk threads. Her mother took a course and received a certificate qualifying her to reel silk. That is how her mother—and later Stella—were able to get hired in Petaluma at the Carlson Currier Silk Mill.

Before her mother moved back to San Francisco, they traveled with the St. Vincent's Parish Ladies by train to Napa. "While our mothers attended a concert at the Opera House, we walked a few blocks south on Main Street to the Hatt building. On the second floor of the brick building, we rented skates and flew across the smooth wooden floors."

I haven't written in a while about the changes in my family. Da got a job back at the new Jackson Brewery last year. Mr. Fredericks made good on his promise that when the new brewery was complete Da could start work again. James finally let it slip that he had been writing to Da and he got permission to return to San Francisco at Christmas. James moved in to Da's bungalow and enrolled in Mission High School. He wants to be a mechanic. Letters from James are rare and usually concern machines. He actually wrote Stella a letter asking if she was at the Carlson Currier Building when the truck carrying silk soap from Pennsylvania had arrived. Across the USA people had been following newspaper accounts of the first cross-country motorized commercial delivery to Petaluma. He wanted an eyewitness account for his term paper at school.

Fiona is 20 now. I can count on a letter from her every month. In May, she wrote to me that with Miss Catherine's help she is going to begin attending classes at the University of California. Fiona intends to win the University Medal like Miss Catherine. She will ride the streetcar to the ferry each morning and return to the Hittell house to do her chores. Mrs. Hittell and Ma would be so proud of her.

Fiona described a Sunday trip to Marin County with Miss Catherine and John Muir's widow, Louisa, to hike the Dipsea Trail to the top of Mount Tamalpais. "While the two ladies shared stories of Mr. Muir, I couldn't keep my eyes off the Pacific Ocean." Fiona sure knows how to tell a story, I could almost see it myself!

October 13, 1913

I woke up earlier than the roosters and the dairy boys and dressed quicker than that fateful night when Father Crowley saved us from the Great Earthquake. I shaved and checked my pocket for the money for the train to Petaluma, the steamer to San Francisco, the meals on board and the streetcar fare.

The half-mile walk to the Rutherford train station took but a few minutes and I boarded the southbound train. After the conductor punched my ticket, I relaxed at the beginning of what I knew would be a special day. I watched the walnut orchards shedding leaves and the neatly laid out farms. From the corner of my eye I spied Mr. Henry Wheatley astride his new stallion, just arrived from England. I haven't even told Da yet that he has offered me a job. I can learn the trade of shoeing because a farrier can work on all the ranches. Mr. Wheatley promised that I would learn animal husbandry and he would give me a place to live. I saw his prune trees for a moment as the train steamed past.

At the Napa Depot the train practically emptied as both men and women rushed to their early shifts in the new factories making shirts, gloves, and blankets. The train filled right up again with farmers and families. We headed east and pulled into

Schellville right on time. I was first off the coach, checked the schedule to make sure the connecting train to Petaluma was due to arrive shortly, and breathed a sigh of relief when I heard the whistle blow.

The grand boat that will carry Stella and me
to San Francisco.

My eyes scanned the crowd. I couldn't contain my smile as I spotted Stella standing next to Mrs. Guiducci on the platform. Stella walked arm in arm with me the short distance to the dock, where we boarded the 10:00 am steamer *Gold* for San Francisco. I paid the 50 cent fare for both of us, along with the 50 cent meal tickets. The porter stowed the large valise with our silk in a secure locker. We found our seats quickly before the steamer pulled away from the dock.

After lunch we went on deck to view the bay with its surface barely ruffled by waves. We could see the small towns wrapping around coves and sometimes crawling up the hills behind them. San Rafael, San Anselmo, and Larkspur disappeared behind us. We sat close together. I dared to put my arm around her shoulder. We daydreamed a bit watching the waves move past us. I told her my plan to accept Mr. Wheatley's offer. Would she ever consider living in Napa? I asked her. I told of the big factories I had seen this morning making gloves and shirts along the Napa River. She shyly told me her dream of owning her own dress shop and sewing silk dresses for rich ladies. Then I did something bold. I gave her a first kiss.

"Alcatraz Island!" bellowed a fat man sitting beside us, and we quickly pulled apart. He explained that right after the earthquake, prisoners were transferred to Alcatraz—everyone calls it "the Rock"—for safety. Just last year the main concrete cellblock of this Federal Prison was completed.

This is as close to Alcatraz as I ever want to get.

After what seemed like the shortest six hours of my life, we landed at Pier 9 in San Francisco. Waiting for us at the station was the Hittell carriage. Mrs. Hittell must be smiling from Heaven to see me riding in her carriage, all grown up, with the fine silk she dreamed we could learn to make. The Land Show is on a lot at Eighth and Market Street where Stella and I both remembered once watching the circus get set up for The Big Show, though neither of us was able to buy a ticket back then.

Like the circus, The Land Show is under a big canvas tent. We walked through the enormous redwood doors carrying our valise. The silk instructor came straightaway to our table where he helped us unfold the silk, both cloth and thread. Now was our time to explore. The floors were covered with wood shavings just like the redwood trees. There is an exhibit from every county in California—grapes, flowers, and livestock. Contra

Costa County, though, has an odd exhibit from Pacific Coast Oil Company [now known as Chevron]. It looks as if they sell oil for the new motor cars that are everywhere. I guess some folks might be interested in that.

I suggested to Stella that we attend the Scottish bagpipers performance—but she wrinkled her nose and agreed only if we could first hear the Hawaiian orchestra. When I was a boy, I had heard bagpipes play at the Youths' Directory, but I could never have imagined the sight and sounds of Hawaiian people.

The best night of my life - Hawaiian band.

Their costumes, musical instruments and dancing left us both dazzled. We wove our way between displays, noticing that some had already received prizes. My heart was beating very fast as I rounded the corner. Stella squeezed my hand when we spied the Blue Ribbon mounted on the display. Our silk was the best in California! Our Carlson Currier Silk will be displayed at the Ferry Building and the Napa Chamber of Commerce.

Ma felt very close to me this evening.

After we danced to the Scottish bagpipes, Stella and I rode to the Hittell home in their carriage to have supper. Just like at my 10th birthday, the large round table was set with crystal and china. We held hands around the table as Father Crowley blessed the meal and I smiled at my much loved family gathered together. Sitting next to me was Stella who filled in the circle. After cake, Da started whistling the Irish Blessing and Father Crowley led the singing:

May the road rise to meet you. May the wind be ever at your back. May the sunshine warm upon your face…

My kit is packed and placed next to the door. The moonlight is just enough for me to finish writing this page. Tomorrow James, in the bunk next to mine, will shake me awake. He and Da will walk with me down Market Street to catch the ferry home. It's been five years since I left for Napa. This time when I say farewell, there will be a train ticket to Rutherford in my pocket!